SONG AND PLAY FOR CHILDREN

FOR SUNDAY AND WEEKDAY USE

FRANCES WELD DANIELSON

AND

GRACE WILBUR CONANT

THE PILGRIM PRESS

BOSTON   CHICAGO

Stanhope Press
F. H. GILSON COMPANY
BOSTON, U.S.A.

FOREWORD

———

RELIGIOUS education has been extended into the week and the summer vacation to a constantly increasing degree since the publication of *Songs for Little People* in 1905, and its revision in 1915. This has created a demand for folk-games, work songs and marches. *Song and Play for Children* shows by its title an attempt to meet this need, as well as to provide more songs of the type of those in the earlier collection.

Realizing the modern emphasis of religion on social relationships, the authors have included many songs of friendliness and service in home and community life, and hymns that awaken the spirit of world brotherhood.

Very short songs for Beginners are grouped in one section for convenience, rather than scattered through the book under the various headings. The single exception is in the department, "Work and Play," which contains games for both Primary children and Beginners.

Other new features are bits of music to inspire desirable moods, a page of children's compositions suggesting the possibilities of self-expression in this line, and a few home songs for use with tiny children.

The old hymns best suited to children appear in *Songs for Little People*, and also the Bible verses that are especially valuable in a musical setting. There are therefore few additions to these in the second book, nor are there new offertories or greeting and farewell songs. There is much supplemental material for worship and for festival seasons, fresh nature songs, and a needed contribution in new hymns picturing the life of the Lord Jesus.

Grateful acknowledgment is made to Milton Bradley Company for use, by special arrangement, of material which originally appeared in *Kindergarten and First Grade* and *Kindergarten Review*, and to The Williams and Wilkins Company for songs from *Childhood Education*.

The authors can ask no more than that the friendly reception still given *Songs for Little People* may be extended to this book, and that they may find a place together on many a teacher's book-shelf.

FRANCES WELD DANIELSON
GRACE WILBUR CONANT

CONTENTS

WORSHIP

FRIENDLINESS AND SERVICE

FESTIVAL SEASONS

MUSIC THAT SUGGESTS VARIOUS MOODS

SONG AND PLAY FOR CHILDREN

WORSHIP

WHEN I AM HAPPIEST

1

FRANCES WELD DANIELSON

GRACE WILBUR CONANT

Not too fast but with strong rhythm

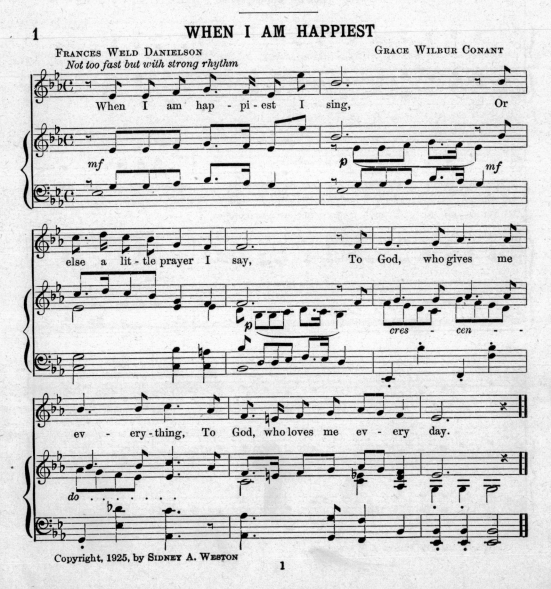

When I am hap-pi-est I sing, Or else a lit-tle prayer I say, To God, who gives me ev-ery-thing, To God, who loves me ev-ery day.

SUNDAY, HAPPY SUNDAY

(The refrain may be used as a short song)

NANCY BYRD TURNER   A. B. PONSONBY

1. When the week has end - ed   To our qui - et homes, With the ear - ly gray light
2. Ev - ery street and lane, then, Ev - ery path and road, Leads us, ea - ger, stead - y,
3. As the weeks are o - ver Hap - py Sun-days come, Sweet in an - y weath - er,

poco rit.   REFRAIN
                                   a tempo

Turn-ing in - to day-light, Bless-ed Sun-day comes.   Sun-day, hap-py Sun - day!
Lov -ing, glad and read - y,   To the house of God.
With us all to - geth - er,   Safe in church and home.

Ev - ery day is dear, But God's day is a bless - ed day, All through the year.

A SONG OF GOD'S HOUSE

NANCY BYRD TURNER   GRACE WILBUR CONANT

With measured, rhythmic movement

mf

1. Glad in the house of God, Up-on his ho-ly day, We lift our hearts in
2. Low in the house of God, Up-on his peace-ful day, With bend-ed heads we

pp

song, His won-drous prais-es say; And while we sing he hears, And when the song is
kneel Our ear-nest prayers to pray; And while we pray he hears, And close, so close, he

poco cres.

done Oh, ver-y, ver-y near he seems To ev-ery list-ening one!
comes, That all the way he walks with us Back to our hap-py homes.

4

OUR DEAR CHURCH

Source unknown

C. H. RINCK

Our dear church was build - ed Long a - go with prayer,

So that all the neigh - bors Might find wel - come there.

5

HOLY, HOLY, HOLY

MARY A. LATHBURY

WILLIAM F. SHERWIN

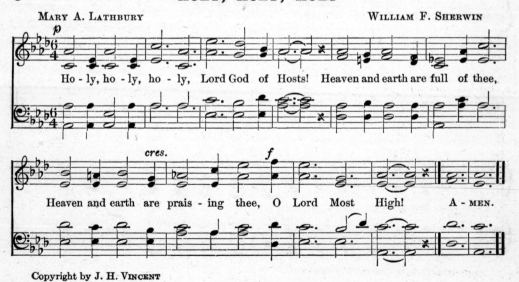

Ho - ly, ho - ly, ho - ly, Lord God of Hosts! Heaven and earth are full of thee,

Heaven and earth are prais - ing thee, O Lord Most High! A - MEN.

4

6 GOD FEEDS THE BIRDS

Katherine Merrill

Schumann, Op. 118

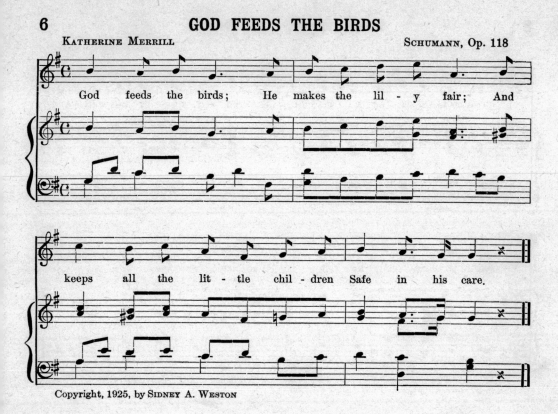

God feeds the birds; He makes the lil - y fair; And keeps all the lit - tle chil - dren Safe in his care.

7 SONG OF PRAISE

Bertha M. Rhodes

A. B. Ponsonby

Ev - ery morn - ing I will raise Un - to God my song of praise, Thank - ing him for hap - py days, — "Glo - ry to the Fa - ther!"

8   **LOVE MADE THE DAISY**

NANCY BYRD TURNER   A. B. PONSONBY
Reverently

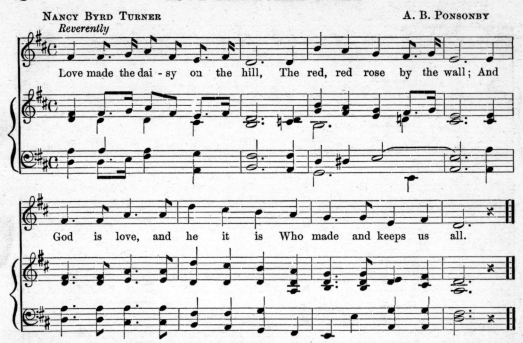

Love made the dai - sy on the hill, The red, red rose by the wall; And

God is love, and he it is Who made and keeps us all.

9   **A CHILD'S GRACE**

FRANCES WELD DANIELSON   A. B. PONSONBY
Moderato

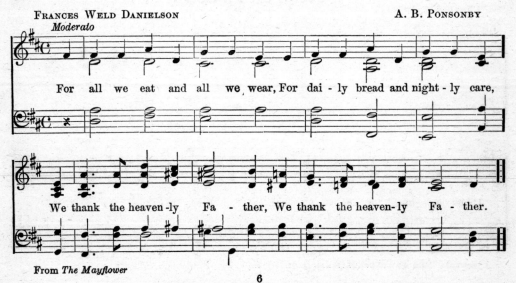

For all we eat and all we wear, For dai - ly bread and night - ly care,

We thank the heaven-ly Fa - ther, We thank the heaven-ly Fa - ther.

From *The Mayflower*

10 SOMETHING HAPPY

Henry van Dyke

A. B. Ponsonby

Ev - ery morn - ing seems to say, "There's some - thing hap - py

marcato

on the way, And God sends love to you!"

Words used by permission of Charles Scribner's Sons. Music from *The Children's Year*, by Grace Wilbur Conant. Used by permission of Milton Bradley Co.

11 BELLS ARE RINGING

OLD FRENCH ROUND IN FOUR PARTS

(This may be sung at first by all the children together, as an ordinary song. When the song is thoroughly familiar they may be divided into four groups and sing it as a round.
(When sung as a round the second group of voices enters at letter **A** when the first group reaches letter **B**, the third group enters at **A** when the second reaches **B**, and so on. When the first group reaches the end of the line **D** it may begin again at **A**.)

Bells are ring - ing, bells are ring - ing,

Loud and clear, loud and clear,

"This is Sun - day morn - ing, this is Sun - day morn - ing!"

Kling, klang, kling, kling, klang, kling!

Copyright, 1925, by Sidney A. Weston

7

TREASURE BOOK

(The first and last stanzas may be sung and the second and third read.)

Frances Weld Danielson   J. H. Wilcox

1. Treas-ure book of chil-dren's sto-ries, Sto-ries old I like to hear!
2. Liv-ing on its glow-ing pag-es Here are man-y friends of mine,
3. Here I find the tale of Je-sus, Help-less Ba-by, thought-ful Boy,
4. Treas-ure book, the ho-ly Bi-ble, Book of sto-ries, old and rare,

Safe with-in en-fold-ing cov-ers They are kept to give us cheer.
Here they work, and here ad-ven-ture,Here they do brave deeds and fine,
Man so kind-ly and so no-ble Foes or hate could not an-noy.
Book that tells the tale of Je-sus, Book that shows the Fa-ther's care;

Or:

Treas-ure book of chil-dren's sto-ries,Treas-ure book,—the Bi-ble dear!
Liv-ing on the glow-ing pag-es Of the Bi-ble, book di-vine!
Here I find the tale of Je-sus, In the Bi-ble, book of joy!
Treas-ure book, the ho-ly Bi-ble, With all chil-dren I would share!

FAR AWAY IN OLD JUDEA

Walter J. Mathams

Gounod

1. Far a-way in old Ju-de-a Lived the gen-tle Lord of Love.
2. Thro' the fields he of-ten led them Where the love-ly lil'-ies grew,
3. Oh, what won-drous tales he told them Of our Fa-ther's thought-ful care;

Hap-py chil-dren gath-ered round him Where-so-ev-er he might move,
Where the crest-ed lark went sing-ing Up-ward to the sky so blue.
How he loves us, leads us, keeps us, Ev-ery day and ev-ery-where;

And they some-times left their play, Just to fol-low him all day.
Thus with him, and birds, and flowers, Glad they spent the gold-en hours.
That we nev-er need to fear, Since his help is al-ways near!

4 With what eager eyes they watched him
   Passing through the crowded street,
Healing all who needed healing,
   Blessing all whom he might meet!
How it made their hearts rejoice
Just to listen to his voice!

5 Not alone in far Judea
   Lived the gentle Lord of Love;
He is now and always with us
   Wheresoever we may move,
And we, too, in toil or play,
Still can follow him all day.

14   WHEN JESUS WAS A LITTLE LAD

Nancy Byrd Turner   Grace Wilbur Conant

Not too fast

1. When Je-sus was a lit-tle lad, In Naz-a-reth of Gal-i-lee,
2. At eve-ning when the tir-ed flocks Came slow-ly down the crook-ed street,

He lis-tened to the wind's low song In ev-ery sway-ing tree.
He pit-ied ev-ery lamb that passed On tim-id, tir-ed feet.

REFRAIN

I dai-ly pray that I shall be Like him of whom the Scrip-tures tell,

That gen-tle boy who loved so well, The lit-tle lad of Gal-i-lee.

3 Not any weary, wounded dove,
    Or small dog homeless in the rain,
  Or frightened hare, or fluttering wren
    Could need his help in vain.

4 His comrades loved him; he was kind
    To younger children when they played;
  And everybody trusted him,
    So true and unafraid.

15   GENTLE CHILD OF NAZARETH

(This is a translation of a hymn said to be sung by the Christian mothers of Palestine. It may be sung without any accompaniment, if desired; or the voices supported only by the melody played in octaves.)

1. Gen - tle child of Naz - a - reth, Let thy life, so meek and ten - der,
2. Wondrous child of Naz - a - reth, Let thy ear - ly love of learn - ing
3. Ho - ly child of Naz - a - reth, Help us use the pow - ers lent us,

Make us glad o - be-dience ren - der To our fa - ther and our moth - er,
Set our youth - ful spir - its yearn - ing Dai - ly to be grow - ing wis - er,
Do the work of Him who sent us, Draw to thee in clos - er un - ion,

And be kind to one an - oth - er, Gen - tle child of Naz - a - reth.
Thou our teach - er and ad - vis - er, Wondrous child of Naz - a - reth.
Share thy peo - ple's sweet commun - ion, Ho - ly child of Naz - a - reth.

THE FIRST CHILDREN'S DAY

Nancy Byrd Turner

Grace Wilbur Conant

1. 'Twas long a - go and far a - way That to a lit - tle town

The Mas - ter came, one sum - mer day, And wea - ry sat him down.

As sun - light fad - ed in the west He sat him down a - while to rest.

REFRAIN

Oh, long a - go and far a - way, But year by year We

hold it dear, That first most love-ly Chil-dren's Day, That first Chil-dren's Day.

2 The mothers whispered each to each:
 "His words are wise and true,
Oh, what if he would bless and teach
 Our little children too!"
And so, before the day grew dim,
They brought the children unto him. REF.

3 He looked into their wondering eyes,
 They looked into his own;
He gathered up the little ones
 Who could not stand alone;
And smiled upon that wistful band,
The older children hand in hand. REF.

4 He spoke, and they were unafraid.
 He told them tenderly
Old stories of another time,
 Old tales of years gone by;
Of boys and girls of other days,
Their gentle hearts, their kindly ways. REF.

5 He told of little Samuel's quick
 Obedience to God's call,
Of Isaac's calm and trusting faith,
 Young Joseph's love for all;
Of Daniel's strong, courageous part,
And little Miriam's faithful heart. REF.

6 He spoke of budding springtime trees;
 Of flowers in the grass;
Of April lambs and building birds
 And winds that blow and pass.
The mothers, watching in their place,
Saw light upon each little face. REF.

7 The children very closely pressed
 And listened, rapt and still.
The youngest baby of them all
 Lay well content, until
As dusky evening shadows crept
Its lashes lowered, and it slept. REF.

8 He blessed them then, and sent them home,
 And they were truly blest,
For as the weeks went by, each child
 Was gentler to the rest,
More watchful of another's need,
More true in word and kind in deed! REF.

17   TELL ME THE STORIES OF JESUS

W. H. Parker

F. A. Challinor

1. Tell me the sto - ries of Je - sus I love to hear; .
2. First let me hear how the chil - dren Stood round his knee; .
3. In - to the cit - y I'd fol - low The chil - dren's band, .
4. Tell me, in ac - cents of won - der, How rolled the sea, .

Things I would ask him to tell me If he were here; Scenes by the
And I shall fan - cy his bless - ing Rest - ing on me; Words full of
Wav - ing a branch of the palm - tree High in my hand; One of his
Toss - ing the boat in a tem - pest On Gal - i - lee! And how the

way - side, Tales of the sea, Sto - ries of Je - sus, Tell them to me.
kind - ness, Deeds full of grace, All in the love - light Of Je - sus' face.
her - alds, Yes, I would sing Loud - est ho - san - nas! Je - sus is King!
Mas - ter, Read - y and kind, Chid - ed the bil - lows, And hushed the wind.

5 Tell how the sparrow that twitters
    On yonder tree
And the sweet meadow-side lily
    May speak to me.
Give me their message,
    For I would hear
How Jesus taught us
    Our Father's care.

6 Show me that scene in the garden,
    Of bitter pain;
And of the cross where my Saviour
    For me was slain.
Sad ones or bright ones,
    So that they be
Stories of Jesus,
    Tell them to me.

THE FATHER'S CARE

18

KATHERINE MERRILL   MISSIONARY SONG   A. B. PONSONBY

All the lit - tle chil - dren, Wher - ev - er they may be, In this land of sun - shine, Or far a - cross the sea, Have a lov - ing Fa - ther, Who, with ten - der care, Watch - es o'er the chil - dren, Here and ev - ery-where.

From *The Mayflower*

GOD'S CHILDREN LIVE IN MANY LANDS

Nancy Byrd Turner

Grace Wilbur Conant

With strong rhythm, but not too fast

mp

1. God's chil-dren live in man-y lands, All scat-tered wide and far,—
2. God's chil-dren speak in dif-ferent tongues, With dif-ferent things to say,

Where nights are long and snow is deep Be-neath the north-ern star;
And dif-ferent tasks and dif-ferent toys, And man-y a dif-ferent way;

Where flow-ers bloom, where riv-ers roll, Where moun-tains tow-er high;
And some are dark, and some are fair, And some are scarce-ly known;

But all with one old earth for home, And un-der one blue sky.
But each is kin to all the rest, And each the Fa-ther's own:

Touch hands a-round the roll-ing world, Call clear, from sea to sea,

That broth-ers, sis-ters are we all In God's great fam-i-ly!

17

FAITHFUL AND STEADY

20

Simplified Salute to the Flag

"We give our heads, our hearts, and our hands to our country. One country, one language, one flag!"

NANCY BYRD TURNER

A. B. PONSONBY

1. Faith - ful and stead - y, Wait - ing we stand; All of us are read - y,
2. Bur - dens for bear - ing, Er - rands to run, Lit - tle tasks for shar - ing,

For we love our land; Glad to be serv - ing; Ea - ger now to start;
Du - ties to be done, Sun - shine for mak - ing Joy in ev - er - y heart;

Oh, we are so will - ing All to do our part!

Words used by permission. Music copyright, 1925, by SIDNEY A. WESTON

21

THE GOOD AMERICAN

With spirit

My coun - try's flag takes care of me; The good A - mer - i - can I will be.

22

ONE LOVELY RULE

NANCY BYRD TURNER

T. A. DORR

1. Learn well one love-ly rule, As true as it is old;
2. This is the rule so good, So gen-tle and so true:

At home, at church, at play, at school, It shines like bur-nished gold.
Do un-to oth-ers as you would That they should do to you.

23

THE HAPPY HEART

Free translation from the German
by FRANCES WELD DANIELSON

Melody by FERD. SCHUBERT

Gaily

1. When lit-tle birds I see I would be sing-ing;
2. When a small bush I see I'd tend it dai-ly,
3. To ev-ery child I see Love I'd be bring-ing;

When lit-tle lambs I see I would be spring-ing.
And with the but-ter-flies I'd dance so gai-ly.
Oh, that the whole wide world With joy were sing-ing!

USEFUL IN THE FAMILY

Nancy Byrd Turner

Grace Wilbur Conant

It is ver-y good to be Use-ful in the fam-i-ly,—

Watch-ing out for oth-ers' needs, Do-ing lit-tle help-ful deeds,

Run-ning er-rands here and there, Speak-ing with a cheer-ful air;

'Tis a pleas-ant thing to be Use-ful in the fam-i-ly.

TAKE GOOD CARE OF MOTHER

Bertha M. Rhodes

A. B. Ponsonby

Not too slowly

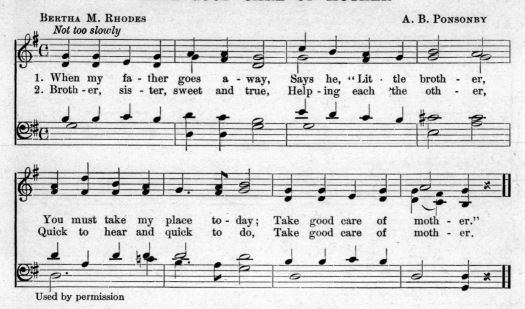

1. When my fa - ther goes a - way, Says he, "Lit - tle broth - er,
2. Broth - er, sis - ter, sweet and true, Help - ing each the oth - er,

You must take my place to - day; Take good care of moth - er."
Quick to hear and quick to do, Take good care of moth - er.

Used by permission

26

DISHES TO WASH

Elizabeth Cushing Taylor

T. A. Dorr

Briskly

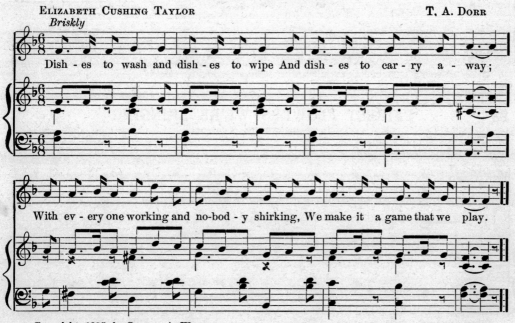

Dish - es to wash and dish - es to wipe And dish - es to car - ry a - way;

With ev - ery one working and no-bod - y shirking, We make it a game that we play.

27

FLOWERS TELL A STORY

(Sung as a child is crowned with flowers, or decorated with garlands, to pay him honor for a brave or kind deed,
or as a birthday attention, or to welcome him after an illness)

ALFARATA HILTON   Polish Folk-song

Flow-ers tell a sto-ry, Tell of danc-ing sun-beams, Flow-ers tell a sto-ry,

Acc. as light as possible

Tell of gen-tle - fin-gered rain,—Oh, lis-ten now, and you will hear it!

Words copyright, 1925, by SIDNEY A. WESTON.   Music used by permission

28

FAIREST FLOWERS WE'RE BRINGING

(To be sung with gifts of flowers)

FRANCES WELD DANIELSON   J. G. NÄGELI

Not too slowly

Fair - est flowers we're bring - ing,   Fair and fra - grant too.

Words copyright, 1925, by SIDNEY A. WESTON

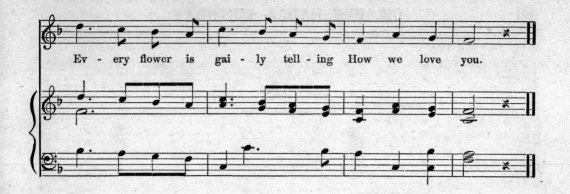

Ev - ery flower is gai - ly tell - ing How we love you.

29   GREEN THINGS GROWING EVERYWHERE

G. W. C.

French Folk-song

Green things grow-ing ev-ery-where In the lit - tle gar-dens, Pret-ty lit- tle gar- dens,

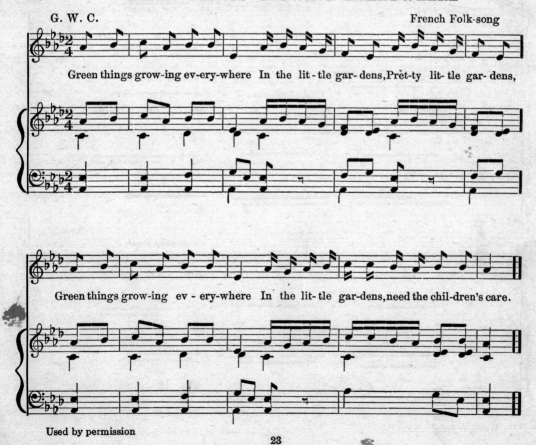

Green things grow-ing ev - ery-where In the lit - tle gar-dens, need the chil-dren's care.

Used by permission

OH, I'VE HAD A BIRTHDAY

Frances Weld Danielson

German Folk-song
17th Century

A single voice

Oh, . I've had a birth-day, I'm eight years to-day!

All the voices

Oh, . he's had a birth-day, he's eight years to-day!

A single voice

May God keep me friend-ly this new year, I pray!

All the voices

May God keep him friend-ly this new year, we pray!

Words copyright, 1925, by Sidney A. Weston. Music used by permission

THANKFUL CHILDREN

31

KATHERINE MERRILL

Bohemian Folk-song

Not too fast

1. Thank - ful chil - dren all are we At this good Thanks-giv - ing time;
2. Thank - ful chil - dren all are we At this good Thanks-giv - ing time;
3. Thank - ful chil - dren all are we At this good Thanks-giv - ing time;

We are thank-ful as can be At this good Thanksgiv- ing time, For our dear
We are thank-ful as can be At this good Thanksgiv- ing time, For our pet
We are thank-ful as can be At this good Thanksgiv- ing time, For fire - sides

lov - ing moth-ers, Fa - thers, sis - ters, broth-ers,— At this good Thanksgiv- ing time.
dogs and kit- tens, Nice warm coats and mit - tens,— At this good Thanksgiv- ing time.
warm and co - zy, Brown nuts and ap - ples ro - sy, — At this good Thanksgiv- ing time.

Used by permission

25

FOR SOWING AND REAPING

Margaret Sangster

Old German Air (1782)

1. For sow - ing and reap - ing, for cold and for heat,
2. For par - ents who care for us day af - ter day,

For sweets of the flow - ers and gold of the wheat,
For sis - ters and broth - ers, for work and for play,

For ships in the har - bors, for sails on the sea,
For dear lit - tle ba - bies so help - less and fair,

Words from *Little Knights and Ladies*, by Margaret Sangster. Used by permission of Harper and Brothers. Music copyright, 1925, by Sidney A. Weston

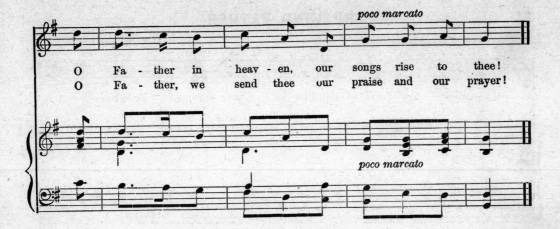

O Fa - ther in heav - en, our songs rise to thee!
O Fa - ther, we send thee our praise and our prayer!

3 For teachers who guide us so patiently on,
For frolics with mates when our lessons are done,
For shelter and clothing, for every day's food,
We bless thee, our Father, the giver of good.

4 For peace and for plenty, for freedom, for rest,
For joy in the land from the east to the west,
For the dear starry flag with its red, white and blue,
We thank thee from hearts that are honest and true.

33   THANKSGIVING RESPONSE

(To be sung repeatedly after mention of the autumn store of food)

ELIZABETH CUSHING TAYLOR   A. B. PONSONBY

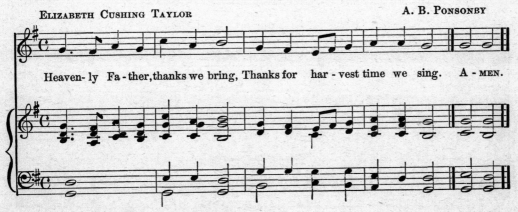

Heaven- ly Fa - ther, thanks we bring, Thanks for har - vest time we sing. A - MEN.

THE KIND FATHER

Frances Weld Danielson

A. B. Ponsonby

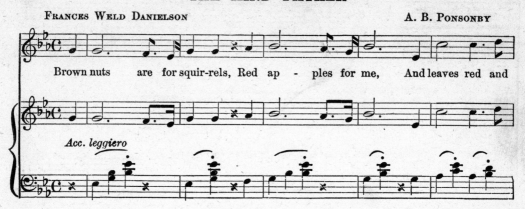

Brown nuts are for squir-rels, Red ap - ples for me, And leaves red and

yel - low For peo - ple to see. I sang in the sum - mer, I

sing in the fall, To God, the kind Fa - ther, Who cares for us all.

largando e poco rit.

From *The Mayflower*

35 BABY JESUS, FAST ASLEEP

Nancy Byrd Turner

Old French Carol

1. Ba - by
2. Lit - tle

p leggiero   mf   acc. leggierissimo p

Je - sus, fast a - sleep, With Ma - ry's face a - bove thee, Shep - herds
child, Wise - men from far Most king - ly pres - ents brought thee; Near thy

piu f

watch - ing o'er their sheep Had an - gel ti - dings of thee. Ba - by
dwell - ing stood the star, All hearts bowed down be - fore thee. With the

cres -

Je - sus, ly - ing fast a - sleep, We come to praise and love thee.
Wise - men com - ing from a - far, We has - ten to a - dore thee.

cen - do   f

Used by permission

29

36 THE BLESSED BABY JESUS

(This old Walloon Noel is perhaps best sung unaccompanied; but for those who prefer some support for the voices an accompaniment is added suggestive of old rustic instruments, some of which had a drone like the bagpipe. The accompaniment should be played very lightly throughout.)

KATHERINE MERRILL

Walloon Carol

1. The bless-ed ba-by Je-sus Was born on Christ-mas day;
2. Now ev-ery Christ-mas morn-ing, For lit-tle Je-sus' sake,

His cra-dle was a man-ger, His pil-low made of hay.
We sing our Christ-mas car-ols And Christ-mas pres-ents make.

The an-gel voic-es were sing-ing; The Wise-men fol-lowed the star,
Sing glo-ry! hal-le-lu-jah! And peace, good-will to men!

And brought to lit-tle Je-sus Rich pres-ents from a-far.
Sing glo-ry! hal-le-lu-jah! And peace on earth a-gain!

THE FRIENDLY BEASTS

XII Century

ROBERT DAVIS

Arranged by CLARENCE DICKINSON

Andantino

Chorus

1. Je - sus, our broth - er, strong and good, Was hum - bly born in a sta - ble rude, And the friend - ly beasts a - round him stood, Je - sus, our broth - er, strong and good.

(Different children take the solo parts.)

Solo:

2 I, said the donkey shaggy and brown,
I carried his mother up hill and down,
I carried her safely to Bethlehem town;
I, said the donkey shaggy and brown.

Solo:

3 I, said the cow all white and red,
I gave him my manger for his bed,
I gave him my hay to pillow his head;
I, said the cow all white and red.

Solo:

4 I, said the sheep with curly horn,
I gave him my wool for his blanket warm,
He wore my coat on Christmas morn;
I, said the sheep with curly horn.

Solo:

5 I, said the dove, from the rafters high,
Cooed him to sleep that he should not cry,
We cooed him to sleep, my mate and I;
I, said the dove, from the rafters high.

Chorus:

6 And every beast, by some good spell,
In the stable dark was glad to tell
Of the gift he gave Immanuel;
The gift he gave Immanuel.

38. LOOK, SHEPHERDS! A LIGHT

Free translation by KATHERINE MERRILL

C. REINECKE

In a manner both joyous and stately

1. Look, shepherds! a light Shines clear thro' the night. From heaven downward winging, The
2. Make haste, shepherds mild, To wel-come the child, Your pipes so soft-ly blowing, With

an - gels come a - sing-ing. Good news, far and near! The Christ-child is here.
love - ly songs o'er - flow-ing. Re - joice, far and near! The Christ-child is here.

Words used by permission

39. THE CHRISTMAS STAR

Author unknown

GRACE WILBUR CONANT

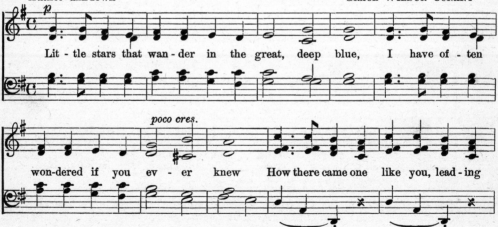

Lit - tle stars that wan - der in the great, deep blue, I have of - ten

poco cres.

won-dered if you ev - er knew How there came one like you, lead-ing

40

OH, COME, LITTLE CHILDREN

KATHERINE MERRILL

Walloon Carol

Joyously

1. Oh, come, lit-tle chil-dren, and joy-ful-ly sing Of the lit-tle Lord Je-sus, our
2. The shepherds were watching their flocks on the hill, The an-gels were sing-ing their

Sav-iour and King! In a man-ger of Beth-le-hem once he was born, On a
song of good-will, Of peace and good-will, when the Sav-iour was born; On a

glad Christ-mas morn, Lit-tle Je-sus was born, Hal-le-lu-jah! Christ was born.

(The questions may be sung by a group of the older ones among the children, or by the teacher or some soloist, the replies of the shepherds by a group of the youngest children. There are possibilities of dramatization in this little dialogue-song.)

G. W. C.   Ancient Noel

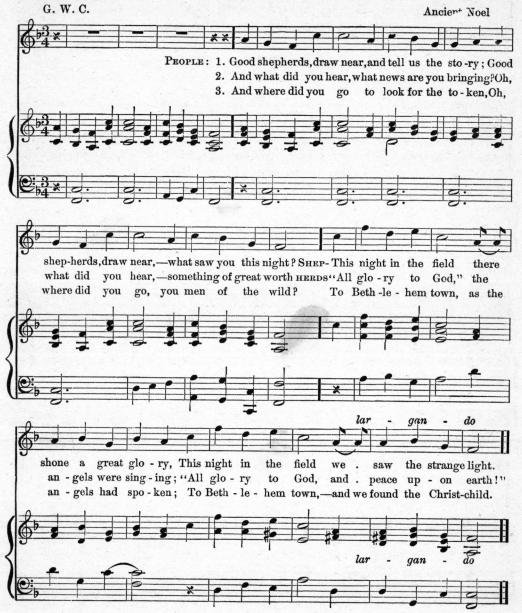

PEOPLE: 1. Good shepherds, draw near, and tell us the sto-ry; Good
2. And what did you hear, what news are you bringing? Oh,
3. And where did you go to look for the to-ken, Oh,

shep-herds, draw near,—what saw you this night? SHEP- This night in the field there
what did you hear,—something of great worth HERDS "All glo-ry to God," the
where did you go, you men of the wild? To Beth-le-hem town, as the

lar - gan - do

shone a great glo-ry, This night in the field we. saw the strange light.
an-gels were sing-ing; "All glo-ry to God, and. peace up-on earth!"
an-gels had spo-ken; To Beth-le-hem town,—and we found the Christ-child.

lar - gan - do

BETHLEHEM

Nancy Byrd Turner

Grace Wilbur Conant

Allegretto

Once there was a lit-tle town Up-on a qui-et hill; There the ba-by Je-sus lay, Ver-y sweet and still. Far a-way and far a-way,—But we praise it, Christ-mas Day; But we praise it, but we praise it, but we praise it, Christmas Day.

(Chimes)

SHINE, CHRISTMAS STAR

Nancy Byrd Turner

Grace Wilbur Conant

Shine, shine, Christ-mas star, Love-ly and far, love-ly and far,

Shine sil-ver-ly o-ver the snow, Glim-mer and glow, glim-mer and glow!

Here in the window our can-dle's a-light, One lit-tle can-dle, so rud-dy and bright.

Look, star, bright and true, Our can-dle is talk-ing to you!

MERRY CHRISTMAS

BERTHA M. RHODES   A. B. PONSONBY

poco rit.   *a tempo*

1. Mer - ry, mer - ry Christ - mas to moth - er dear! Lov - ing moth - er,
2. Mer - ry, mer - ry Christ - mas to fa - ther dear! Gen - tle fa - ther,
3. Mer - ry, mer - ry Christ - mas to broth - er dear! Christ - mas can - dles
4. Mer - ry, mer - ry Christ - mas to sis - ter dear! Shin - ing bright, the
5. Mer - ry, mer - ry Christ - mas we wish to all! Lit - tle chil - dren

mf   *poco rit.*   *p a tempo*

wise to know How a lit - tle child should grow,—Mer - ry, mer - ry Christ - mas,
tall and strong, Work - ing for us all day long,—Mer - ry, mer - ry Christ - mas,
burn - ing bright Light the Christ - child through the night. Mer - ry, mer - ry Christ - mas,
Christ - mas star Sheds its hap - py beams a - far. Mer - ry, mer - ry Christ - mas,
wake to say, "This is hap - py Christ - mas Day." Mer - ry, mer - ry Christ - mas,

mp

poco rit.

Mer - ry, mer - ry Christ - mas, Mer - ry, mer - ry Christ - mas to moth - er dear!
Mer - ry, mer - ry Christ - mas, Mer - ry, mer - ry Christ - mas to fa - ther dear!
Mer - ry, mer - ry Christ - mas, Mer - ry, mer - ry Christ - mas to broth - er dear!
Mer - ry, mer - ry Christ - mas, Mer - ry, mer - ry Christ - mas to sis - ter dear!
Mer - ry, mer - ry Christ - mas, Mer - ry, mer - ry Christ - mas we wish to all!

f   *poco rit.*

Used by permission

THE CHRISTMAS TREE

(After the song the children may join hands and circle around the tree.)

NANCY BYRD TURNER   GRACE WILBUR CONANT

Mer - ri - ly, mer - ri - ly, Tell of the Christ - mas tree, Toys in the branch - es And toys at the root! Mer - ri - ly, mer - ri - ly, Sing of the Christ - mas tree! When did a tree bear Such won - der - ful fruit?

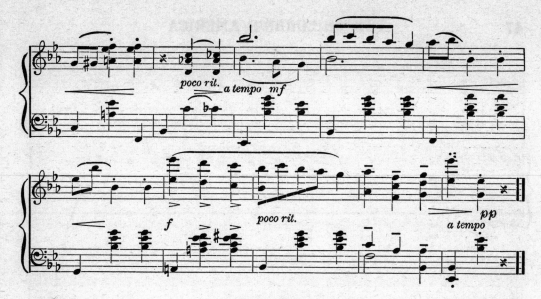

46

FOR MOTHER

Words and melody by BERTHA M. RHODES

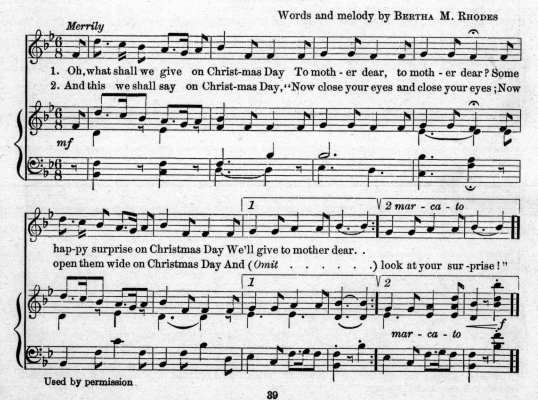

1. Oh, what shall we give on Christ-mas Day To moth - er dear, to moth - er dear? Some
2. And this we shall say on Christ-mas Day, "Now close your eyes and close your eyes; Now

hap-py surprise on Christmas Day We'll give to mother dear. .
open them wide on Christmas Day And (*Omit* . . . .) look at your sur -prise!"

THE CHILDREN'S AMERICA

Alfarata Hilton

A. B. Ponsonby

With spirit

1. A - mer - i - ca, A - mer - i - ca! Our hearts be - long to thee;
2. A - mer - i - ca, A - mer - i - ca! Our hearts be - long to thee;

mf

For fer - tile fields and riv - ers wide And cit - ies fair to see.
For school and church and hap - py homes, For friends and fam - i - ly.

Refrain

A - mer - i - ca, A - mer - i - ca! A pleas - ant land to see,
A - mer - i - ca, A - mer - i - ca! A friend - ly place to be,

mf

cres - - cen - - do mol - to

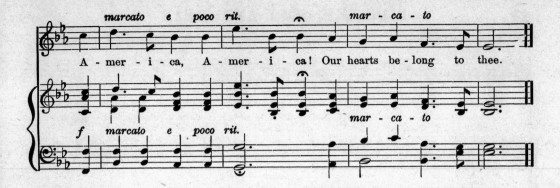

marcato e poco rit.   mar - ca - to

A - mer - i - ca, A - mer - i - ca! Our hearts be - long to thee.

f   marcato e poco rit.   mar - ca - to

48   MY COUNTRY, 'TIS OF THEE
AMERICA

SAMUEL F. SMITH   HENRY CAREY

1. My coun - try, 'tis of thee, Sweet land of lib - er - ty,
2. My na - tive coun - try, thee, Land of the no - ble free,
3. Let mu - sic swell the breeze, And ring from all the trees
4. Our fa - thers' God, to thee, Au - thor of lib - er - ty,

Of thee I sing; Land where my fa - thers died, Land of the
Thy name I love; I love thy rocks and rills, Thy woods and
Sweet free - dom's song; Let mor - tal tongues a - wake; Let all that
To thee we sing; Long may our land be bright With free - dom's

pil - grims' pride, From ev - ery moun - tain - side Let free - dom ring!
tem - pled hills; My heart with rap - ture thrills Like that a - bove.
breathe par - take; Let rocks their si - lence break, The sound pro - long.
ho - ly light; Pro - tect us by thy might, Great God, our King.

BLUE SKY, SOFT AND CLEAR

A. R. MINTER   EASTER SONG   Bohemian Folk-song

Moderato

1. Blue sky, soft and clear, Bird songs, far and near, Gay lit - tle blades of grass
2. Blue sky, soft and clear, Bird songs, far and near; Lift up your shin - ing head,
3. Blue sky, soft and clear, Bird songs, far and near; God gives the sun and rain,

p *pp* *cres* - - -

Nod as the chil - dren pass,—East-er is here, East - er is here!
Flower that we thought was dead,—East-er is here, East - er is here!
God brings back life a - gain,—East-er is here, East - er is here!

cen - - *do* *f* *p*

Words copyright, 1925, by SIDNEY A. WESTON

50   SLEEP, LITTLE SEED

LOUISE M. OGLEVEE   W. G. OGLEVEE

1. Sleep, sleep, sleep, lit - tle seed, Sleep through the win - ter long.
2. Sleep, sleep, sleep, lit - tle seed, Hid - den from sight a - way.

Wake, wake, wake in the spring, Wake with the blue - bird's song.
Wake, wake, wak - en and grow, Wak - en for East - er Day.

THE BELLS OF EASTER

KATHERINE MERRILL

A. B. PONSONBY

1. The bells of East-er sweet-ly ring, And lit-tle chil-dren
2. For Christ is ris-en from the dead, And ev-er-y flower lifts

sweet-ly sing, While all the love-ly flow-ers gay Are sing-ing songs of
up its head, While all the bells of East-er ring, And lit-tle chil-dren

joy to-day,— Sing-ing, sing-ing, songs of joy to-day.
sweet-ly sing,— Chil-dren, chil-dren, chil-dren sweet-ly sing.

LITTLE PAGEANT FOR ARBOR DAY

MARCH PRELUDE

Grace Wilbur Conant

Words from *Lyrics of Love*, by Margaret Sangster.   Used by permission of Fleming H. Revell Co.
Music copyright, 1925, by Sidney A. Weston

LITTLE PAGEANT FOR ARBOR DAY

MARGARET SANGSTER   SONG   G. W. C.

We are plant-ing a tree,—For to - day and to - mor -row, For the blithe years to be, For the com - fort of sor -row, For shel - ter and shade, For the song and the wing, For the sun and the rain And the sweet showers of spring, For sum - mers and au -tumns And win -ters to be, For storms and for calms, We are planting a tree.

FLOWER SONG FOR MEMORIAL DAY

Nancy Byrd Turner   Grace Wilbur Conant

Gravely and deliberately

1. Grow, wee vi - o - let; bloom, fair rose!
2. Smile, blue vi - o - let; shine, red rose!

Ferns, un - curl, when the warm wind blows! Lit-tle buds sleep - ing, hur - ry, a - wake,
Flut- ter, ferns, when the warm wind blows! Bright on the green mounds beau - ty make,

Do your part for the sol -diers' sake— Do your part for the sol- diers' sake!
All this day for the sol -diers' sake— All this day for the sol- diers' sake!

54

CHILDREN WHO WALK IN JESUS' WAY

PROCESSIONAL FOR CHILDREN'S DAY

Nancy Byrd Turner   Grace Wilbur Conant

With strong rhythm but not too fast

1. Chil - dren who walk in Je - sus' way, . Light shall go
2. Chil - dren who choose him as . . their guide. Keep the good .
3. Chil - dren who march where Je - sus leads, . They . shall be

with them, day by . day; . . They shall be free, .
road what - e'er be - tide; . . They shall be strong, .
his in thoughts and . deeds; . They shall have love, .

they shall be glad, Chil - dren who walk in Je - sus' way.
they shall be safe, Chil - dren who choose him as . . their guide.
they shall have joy, Chil - dren who march where Je - sus leads.

SING, YE HAPPY CHILDREN

E. E. HEWITT
Not too fast

W. C. LEVEY
Arr. by GEO. B. NEVIN

1. Sing, ye hap-py chil-dren, sing with glad-ness; Let your sweet ho-san-nas rise a-bove. Sum-mer's gold-en sun-beams ban-ish sad-ness, For they seem to tell us God is love. Let us join in tell-ing na-ture's sto-ry, Told so sweet-ly, o'er and o'er. Wood-land, field and mea-dow show his glo-ry, Sing his prais-es ev-er-more. Sing, ye hap-py chil-dren,

2. Sing, ye hap-py chil-dren, free-ly bring-ing Joy-ful hearts and voic-es this blest hour, While from wren and rob-in songs are ring-ing, Sing our Fa-ther's good-ness, sing his power. He it is who gives us pleas-ant sea-sons, All that makes this earth so fair. Grat-i-tude will find a-bun-dant rea-sons For the songs that fill the air.

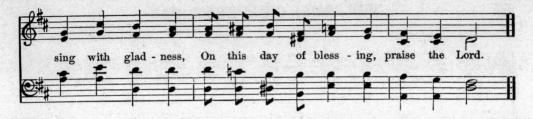

sing with glad - ness, On this day of bless - ing, praise the Lord.

56 PRAISE GOD ON CHILDREN'S DAY

(A small group with good voices may sing this song, all the children joining in the line, "Praise God, on Children's Day," whenever it occurs.)

D. C. M.

Béarnaise Melody

Come, sing a song of greet - ing,—Praise God on Chil-dren's Day!
Glad in his house we're meet -ing,—Praise God on Chil-dren's Day!

Praise him for sum - mer weath - er, Praise him for flow - ers gay;

Chil - dren and friends to - geth - er Praise God on Chil-dren's Day.

Words copyright, 1925, by Sidney A. Weston. Music used by permission

WELCOME, CHILDREN'S DAY

Alfarata Hilton

A. B. Ponsonby

Allegretto

1. The sun is shin - ing high a - bove, Sweet flowers are ev - ery - where, The
2. From far and near with lov - ing hearts To - day we've gath - ered here To

birds pour out their mu - sic Up - on the fra - grant air, While joy - ful bells the
praise the heaven - ly Fa - ther, Who holds all chil - dren dear. We lift our voic - es

REFRAIN

mes - sage ring And hap - py voic - es join and sing, Wel - come, Children's Day !
clear and strong, And of - fer him our sweet - est song,—

Wel - come, Chil - dren's Day ! Sing, sing, sing, Wel - come, Children's Day !

WHAT THE SEASONS BRING

A SONG FOR ALL THE YEAR ROUND

58

Gertrude Maynard

Old German Folk-song

1. What does au - tumn bring me,— Gold - en au - tumn
2. What does win - ter bring me,— Frost - y win - ter
3. What does spring - time bring me,— Love - ly spring - time
4. What does sum - mer bring me,— Hap - py sum - mer

bring me? Ro - sy ap - ples, oh, so sweet, Peach - es, plums and
bring me? Snow and ice and jol - ly fun, Christ - mas joy for
bring me? Lit - tle vio - lets in the grass, Rob - in sing - ing
bring me? Bees that hum a - mong the flowers, Play through all the

grapes to eat: This does au - tumn bring me.
ev - ery one: This does win - ter bring me.
as I pass: This does spring - time bring me.
sun - ny hours: This does sum - mer bring me.

TWO LITTLE BIRDS

Author unknown

As if telling a story

GRACE WILBUR CONANT

Two lit - tle birds, one au - tumn day, Sat on a tree to - geth - er. They
flut - tered a - bout from bough to bough And talked a - bout the weath - er. "The
wind is blow-ing so cold," said they, "It chills us as we sing." So a -
way they flew to the sun - ny south, And there they stayed till spring; So a -

way they flew to the sun-ny south, And there they stayed till spring.

60   **FALLING LEAVES**

NANCY BYRD TURNER   GRACE WILBUR CONANT

Ver - y yel - low, ver - y brown, Ver - y bright and red,

Pat - ter, pat - ter, pat - ter down On my head.

Gold and crim - son, Buff and brown, Pat - ter down!

53

WELCOME TO AUTUMN

Nancy Byrd Turner

A. B. Ponsonby

With spirit

1. In gar - den, field and mead - ow The grass is crisp and curled, A
2. God gave us hap - py sum - mer, He gave us love - ly spring, And

cross the chill - y hill - tops The swift high winds are whirled. There's
win - ter nights and morn - ings, With all the joy they bring. Now

red on all the leaves, The corn's in gold - en . sheaves, And
au - tumn days are come, And bless - ed har - vest . home, We

sil - ver frost is sharp and bright Up -on the old brown world.
lift our hearts to wel-come them, And (*Omit* . . . .) sing, sing, sing.

THE BIRDS' FLIGHT

(Use either form of words given in the second measure, according to the season.)

G. W. C.

Norwegian Folk-song

Now the birds fly from the win-ter-time, From its chil-ly snow and rain;
(birds have flown)

But the win-ter will soon be o-ver, And the birds will come back a-gain.

Used by permission

A WINTER DAY

Frances Felber Weld

Slav Folk-song

With spirit

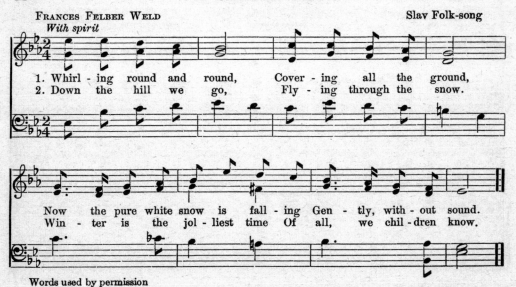

1. Whirl-ing round and round, Cover-ing all the ground,
2. Down the hill we go, Fly-ing through the snow.

Now the pure white snow is fall-ing Gen-tly, with-out sound.
Win-ter is the jol-liest time Of all, we chil-dren know.

Words used by permission

WINTER SONG

Nancy Byrd Turner

Grace Wilbur Conant

1. There's frost on the hill, There's snow in the air, The birds are all still, And the boughs are all bare; But bright in our homes Burn fires of cheer. Win-ter's a beau-ti-ful Time of the year! Win-ter's a beau-ti-ful Time of the year!

2. The wind's sing-ing on, Though the bird songs are dumb, The flow-ers are gone, But the snow-flakes are come. By day and by night, God seems ver-y near. Win-ter's a won-der-ful Time of the year! Win-ter's a won-der-ful Time of the year!

BLOW, WIND

NANCY BYRD TURNER

GERTRUDE MAYNARD

Vigorously

Blow, wind, blow up and down, O - ver the

coun - try and o - ver the town; Blow, good wind, and

sing me a song . . . . All the

day long!

Used by permission

KEEP THOU OUR GARDEN

Nancy Byrd Turner

A. B. Ponsonby

Here, Lord, our seeds we're sow-ing. Send rain and sun up - on them; Set winds a-

bove them blowing; Let harm and dan - ger shun them. Bring flower and precious food

Forth from the fra-grant sod; Make thou our har-vest good, Keep thou our

poco rit.   *reverently and more slowly*

gar - den, God! Make thou our har - vest good, Keep thou our gar - den, God!

poco rit.   *reverently and more slowly*

GREEN IN ALL THE MEADOWS

NANCY BYRD TURNER

A. B. PONSONBY

Gaily

1. Green in all the mead-ows, Green be-side the shore,
2. Blue on hill and moun-tain, Blue in sky and sea,

Flowers in the gar-den, Flowers by the door; Ev-ery year we meet her,
Birds in all the tree-tops Sing-ing joy-ful-ly; Ev-ery year we meet her,

Ev-ery time we greet her, Some-how spring is sweet-er Than she was be-fore.
Ev-ery time we greet her, Spring is sure-ly sweet-er Than she used to be.

68   THE SWALLOW

(Appropriate for dramatization)

MARIAN DOUGLAS   GRACE WILBUR CONANT

With quick, tripping movement

The li-lacs are in blos-som, The cher-ry flowers are white;

I hear a sound a-bove me, A twit-ter of de-light.

joyously, and a trifle less fast   *a tempo*

It is my friend the swal-low, As sure as I'm a-live!

poco rit.

I'm ver-y glad to see you. Pray, when did you ar-rive?

Used by permission

60

A SUMMER HYMN

NANCY BYRD TURNER

A. B. PONSONBY

1. Al - ways earth is ver - y fair, God, whose name we praise; With the snow up -
2. All the year is ver - y fair, God, to whom we sing; Take our thanks for

on it, In Sep-tem-ber's haze, When the A - pril rain-drops Soft - ly on it fall;
win- ter, Take our thanks for spring, Take our praise for autumn, When the bright leaves fall;

poco rit.

But in light of sum -mer It's love - li - est of a.l, It's love - li - est of all!
But for hap- py sum -mer We thank thee most of all, We thank thee most of all!

poco rit.

70 ## THE WEE BIRD IN THE WILLOW

Nancy Byrd Turner

Grace Wilbur Conant

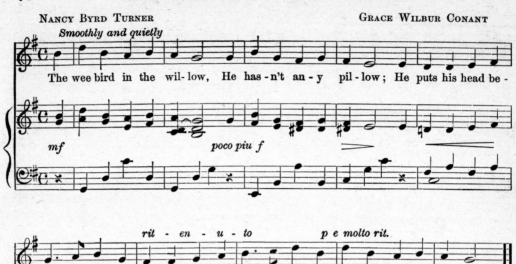

The wee bird in the wil-low, He has-n't an-y pil-low; He puts his head be-

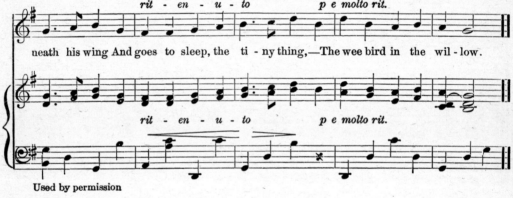

neath his wing And goes to sleep, the ti-ny thing,—The wee bird in the wil-low.

Used by permission

71 ## THE ROSE

Ruth Brewer

Grace Wilbur Conant

Out in the gar-den blooms the rose,

Used by permission

Sweet-est flower that ev-er grows,—Sweet-est flower that grows.

cres - cen - do   *poco rit.*   *a tempo*

marcato
più f

72   **SUMMER SUN**

ROBERT LOUIS STEVENSON   GRACE WILBUR CONANT

Great is the sun, and wide he goes Through emp-ty heaven with-out re-pose;

f Like a stately march

And in the blue and glow-ing days More thick than rain he showers his rays.

Words from *A Child's Garden of Verses*, by ROBERT LOUIS STEVENSON.   Used by permission of CHARLES
SCRIBNER'S SONS. Music copyright, 1924, by SIDNEY A. WESTON

63

HOW GAY AND BRIGHT

BERTHA M. RHODES

T. A. DORR

With the utmost lightness

1. How gay and bright, how fair and light, A cloud - let sails a - way, Wher-
2. He skims the brook be - neath the trees, He flies a - gainst the breeze; He
3. The heaven - ly Fa - ther gives him wings, He gives the song he sings; When

mf

e'er the winds shall har - bor it, While soft its shad - ows play.
floats with clouds that sail on high And sings in sum - mer sky.
shades of eve - ning soft - ly creep Gives child and bird - ling sleep.

REFRAIN

But no winds can say and no child can know Where a lit - tle bird will go,

p

poco rit.

No winds can say and no child can know Where a lit - tle bird will go.

poco rit.

poco cres.

dim.

p

Words used by permission of BERTHA M. RHODES. Music copyright, 1925, by SIDNEY A. WESTON

SING A SONG OF SEASONS

ROBERT LOUIS STEVENSON

T. A. DORR

Sing a song of sea-sons! Some-thing bright in all!

poco rit.

Flowers in the sum-mer, Fires in the fall!

poco rit.

Words from *A Child's Garden of Verses*, by ROBERT LOUIS STEVENSON. Used by permission of CHARLES SCRIBNER'S SONS. Music copyright, 1925, by SIDNEY A. WESTON

MY BRIGHT RED APPLE

Tr. G. W. C.

German Kindergarten Song

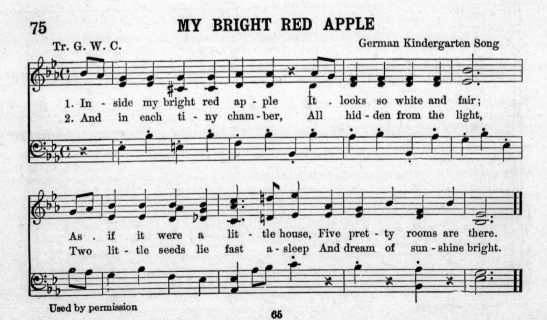

1. In-side my bright red ap-ple It looks so white and fair;
2. And in each ti-ny cham-ber, All hid-den from the light,

As if it were a lit-tle house, Five pret-ty rooms are there.
Two lit-tle seeds lie fast a-sleep And dream of sun-shine bright.

Used by permission

KITTY'S SONG

Nancy Byrd Turner
Allegretto

Grace Wilbur Conant

Kit - ty cat, I'll smooth your fur, Smooth your fur,

If you'll teach me how to purr, How to purr.

Purr, purr, loud and strong,—Who could learn a kit - ty's song?

Purr, purr, loud and strong, Purr, purr, purr!

77 "GOD IS MY HELPER"

Nancy Byrd Turner   Grace Wilbur Conant

1. "God is my help - er," this . . I know, What-
2. When I wake ear - ly, this is my song: . .

ev - er I do and wher - ev - er I go.
"'God is my help - er' the whole . day long."

From *The Pilgrim Elementary Teacher*

78 A WEE PRAYER

Edith C. Rice   G. W. C.

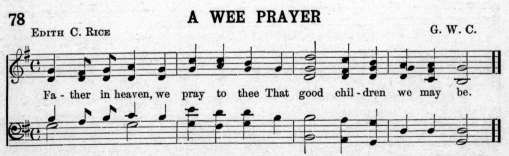

Fa - ther in heaven, we pray to thee That good chil - dren we may be.

From *The Children's Year*, by Grace Wilbur Conant. Used by permission of Milton Bradley Co.

IN TINY NESTS

NANCY BYRD TURNER

GRACE WILBUR CONANT

In ti-ny nests a-mong the leaves, In bush and tree and shel-tered eaves,

All warm and safe and un-a-fraid— God loves so well the birds he made!

marcato e poco rit.

From THE CONGREGATIONAL SUNDAY-SCHOOL EXTENSION SOCIETY

80 WHEN JESUS WALKED THIS EARTH OF OURS

NANCY BYRD TURNER

G. W. C.

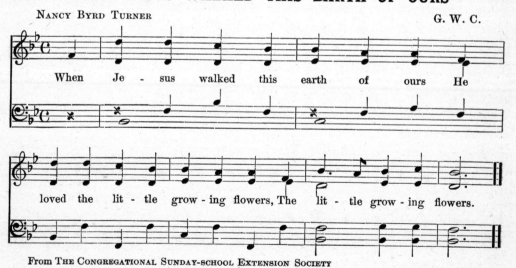

When Je - sus walked this earth of ours He

loved the lit - tle grow-ing flowers, The lit - tle grow-ing flowers.

From THE CONGREGATIONAL SUNDAY-SCHOOL EXTENSION SOCIETY

81

THE CHURCH BELLS

D. M.

T. A. DORR

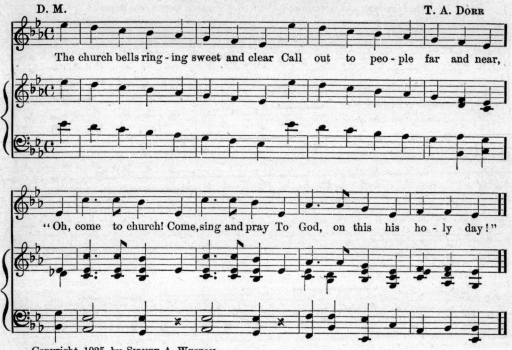

The church bells ring-ing sweet and clear Call out to peo-ple far and near,

"Oh, come to church! Come, sing and pray To God, on this his ho-ly day!"

82

PRAISE SONG

FRANCES WELD DANIELSON

GRACE WILBUR CONANT

Reverently

We thank the heaven-ly Fa - ther, We thank the heaven - ly

Fa - ther, We thank the heaven-ly Fa - ther, kind and good.

83

MY FAMILY

(The finger play may be commenced with the first finger, omitting the thumb.)

GERTRUDE MAYNARD

Bohemian Folk-song

Do you see my fam-i-ly here? Fa-ther, moth-er, sis-ter, broth-er,

Oh, how well they love each oth-er! Do you see my fam-i-ly dear?

Used by permission

84

BIRTHDAY CHILD

From a Breton Folk-tune

Birth-day Child, to you we sing,— Hap-py birth-day greet-ing!

Copyright, 1925, by SIDNEY A. WESTON

70

85   MOTHER BIRDS

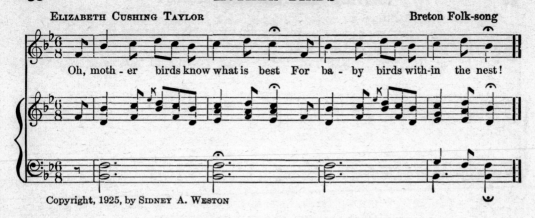

ELIZABETH CUSHING TAYLOR   Breton Folk-song

Oh, moth - er birds know what is best For ba - by birds with-in the nest!

86   MOTHER CALLS US IN THE MORNING

ELIZABETH CUSHING TAYLOR   GRACE WILBUR CONANT

Briskly

Moth - er calls us in the morn - ing When the sun is high;

When we go to bed at night Stars are in the sky.

87 FATHER MAKES THE MONEY

FRANCES WELD DANIELSON

T. A. DORR

Fa - ther makes the mon - ey, Moth - er cooks the food,

Hap - py lit - tle chil - dren help by be - ing good.

Copyright, 1925, by SIDNEY A. WESTON

88 TICK, TOCK

R. A. MINTER

From a German Folk-song

Lightly

"Tick, tock, tick, tock," sings the clock, "If you wait, You'll be late."

"Tick, tock, tick, tock," sings the clock, Sings our friend the clock.

Used by permission

72

89

MY SHINY SHOES
(Clothing worn by the children should be substituted.)

Frances Weld Danielson

A. B. Ponsonby

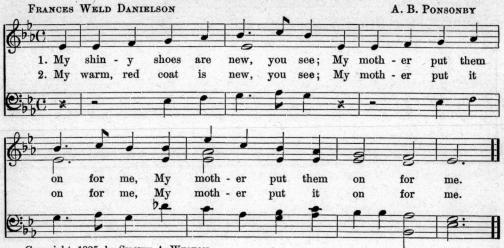

1. My shin-y shoes are new, you see; My moth-er put them on for me, My moth-er put them on for me.
2. My warm, red coat is new, you see; My moth-er put it on for me, My moth-er put it on for me.

90

O GRANDMOTHER, TELL ME
(One child impersonates the grandmother. The others sing to her, and she suggests bringing her shawl, or fanning her, or doing an errand, which they act out in pantomime.)

Frances Weld Danielson

A. B. Ponsonby

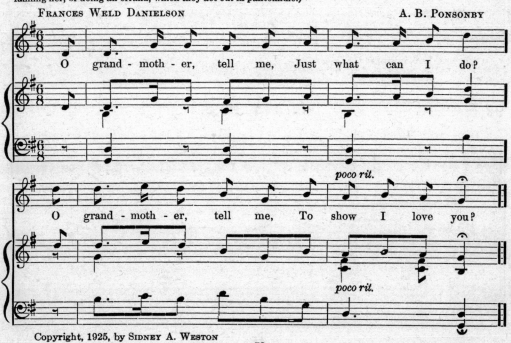

O grand-moth-er, tell me, Just what can I do?

O grand-moth-er, tell me, To show I love you?

poco rit.

91

WHAT CAN I DO?

(After singing this, the children show in pantomime helpful acts and tell words that give pleasure, such as "please" and "thank you.")

FRANCES WELD DANIELSON

T. A. DORR

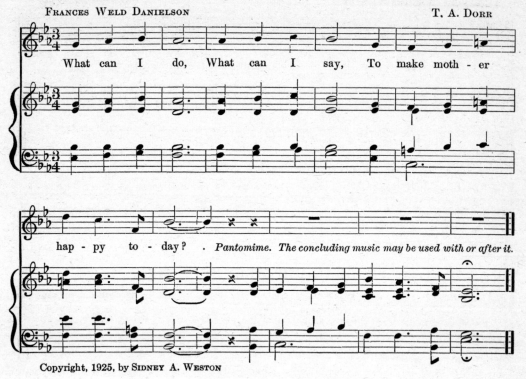

What can I do, What can I say, To make moth - er hap - py to - day? . *Pantomime. The concluding music may be used with or after it.*

92

PRETTY PUSS

KATHERINE MERRILL

Folk-song from Languedoc

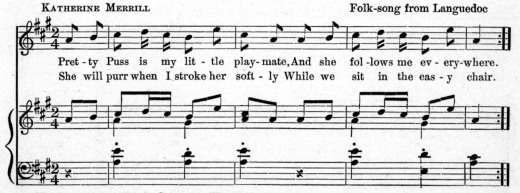

Pret - ty Puss is my lit - tle play-mate, And she fol -lows me ev - ery-where.
She will purr when I stroke her soft - ly While we sit in the eas - y chair.

93

BIRDS IN WINTER

(This may be dramatized.)

Bertha M. Rhodes   German Folk-song

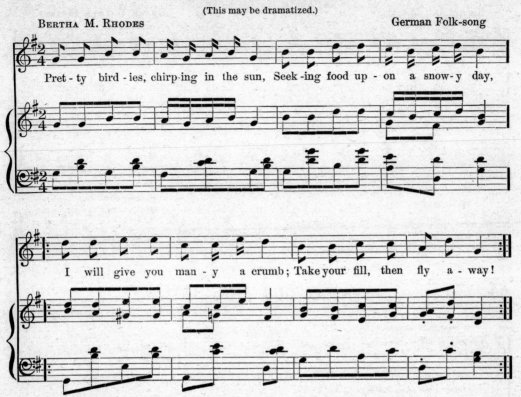

Pret-ty bird-ies, chirp-ing in the sun, Seek-ing food up-on a snow-y day,

I will give you man-y a crumb; Take your fill, then fly a-way!

Copyright, 1918, by Congregational Sunday-school and Publishing Society

94

THE GOOD RED HEN

Katherine Merrill   G. W. C.

The good red hen has yel-low feet; She gives us nice fresh eggs to eat.

Copyright, 1925, by Sidney A. Weston

OUR BUNNY'S SO FUNNY

KATHERINE MERRILL

GRACE WILBUR CONANT

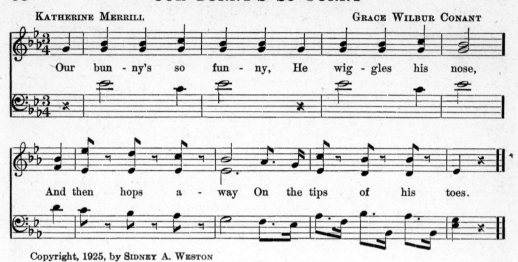

Our bun-ny's so fun-ny, He wig-gles his nose,

And then hops a - way On the tips of his toes.

96

WHAT OUR PETS SAY

KATHERINE MERRILL
Very rhythmically

GRACE WILBUR CONANT

The dog says, "Bow wow, Come play with me now!" The bird says, "I'll sing, If

The cat says, "I'll purr, If you'll stroke my fur."

bird - seed you'll bring." The gold - fish can't speak, But play hide - and - seek.

MOTHER GOOSE AND FATHER GANDER

Katherine Merrill

Grace Wilbur Conant

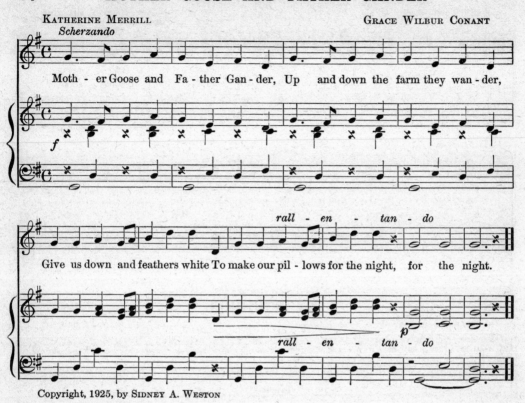

Moth - er Goose and Fa - ther Gan - der, Up and down the farm they wan - der,

Give us down and feathers white To make our pil - lows for the night, for the night.

THE LITTLE BUSY BEE

Katherine Merrill

G. W. C.

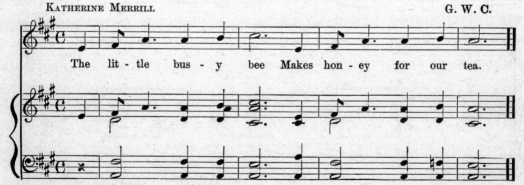

The lit - tle bus - y bee Makes hon - ey for our tea.

99

I LOVE LITTLE PUSSY

JANE TAYLOR

Arr. from E. SILCHER

1. I love lit - tle pus - sy, her coat is . so . warm,
2. I'll sit by her side, and I'll give her some food,

And . if I don't tease her, she'll do me no harm.
And she'll love me be - cause I am gen - tle and good.

100

MY SQUIRREL

GERTRUDE MAYNARD

French Air

Here comes my lit - tle squir - rel, Dressed all in fur - ry gray;

He takes my nut so quick - ly, Then hides it safe a - way.

101   IN GRANDPA'S BARN

ELIZABETH CUSHING TAYLOR

A. B. PONSONBY

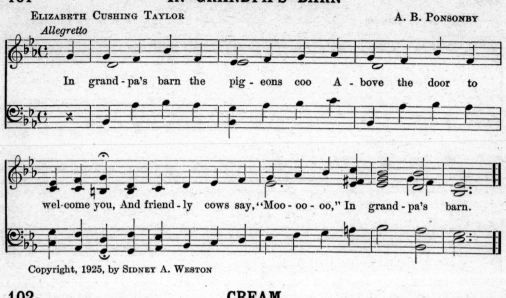

In grand-pa's barn the pig-eons coo A-bove the door to wel-come you, And friend-ly cows say, "Moo-oo-oo," In grand-pa's barn.

102   CREAM

NANCY BYRD TURNER

GRACE WILBUR CONANT

Cream from the red cow, Cream from the white; Ev-ery one can have a bowl Of bread and milk to-night.

103 STILL AND WHITE

Nancy Byrd Turner

Grace Wilbur Conant

Lit - tle, light, All the night Flakes come fall - ing, Still and white.

Acc. leggierissimo

poco rit.

Soft as flour In a mill, See them on The win - dow - sill!

poco rit.

Used by permission

104 SNOWFLAKES

Words and music by Beth Noxon

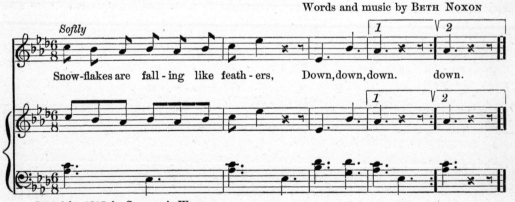

Snow-flakes are fall - ing like feath - ers, Down, down, down. down.

Copyright, 1925, by Sidney A. Weston

105   RAIN, RAIN

(The children may vary the second line, as, " Make the grass all green again.")

Author unknown   A. B. P.

Rain, rain, spring-time rain! Bring the flow-ers back a-gain.

Copyright, 1925, by Sidney A. Weston

106   PUSSY WILLOW

Words and music by Beth Noxon

Quick and lively

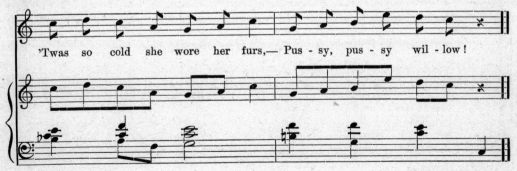

Pus-sy wil-low, soft and gray, Paid her first spring call to-day;

'Twas so cold she wore her furs,— Pus-sy, pus-sy wil-low!

Used by permission

107   OH, SING, SING, SING

R. A. Minter

Schubert

"Oh, sing, sing, sing!" The flow - ers seem to say.

"Oh, sing, sing, sing! For this is East - er Day."

108   HOME

Herbert Scholfield

Grace Wilbur Conant

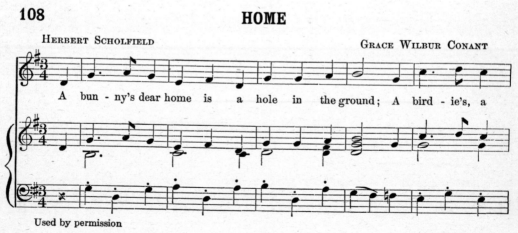

A bun - ny's dear home is a hole in the ground; A bird - ie's, a

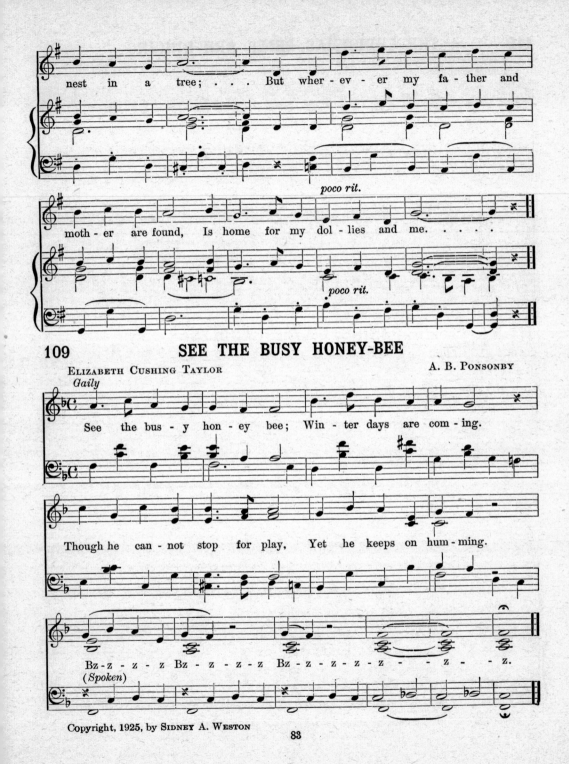

nest in a tree; ... But wher-ev-er my fa-ther and mother are found, Is home for my dol-lies and me. ....

poco rit.

109 SEE THE BUSY HONEY-BEE

ELIZABETH CUSHING TAYLOR

A. B. PONSONBY

Gaily

See the bus-y hon-ey bee; Win-ter days are com-ing.

Though he can-not stop for play, Yet he keeps on hum-ming.

Bz-z-z-z Bz-z-z-z Bz-z-z-z-z - z - z.
(Spoken)

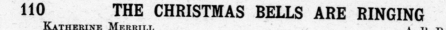

110 THE CHRISTMAS BELLS ARE RINGING

KATHERINE MERRILL

A. B. PONSONBY

With simplicity

The Christ-mas bells are ring - ing And this is what they say:

mar - ca - to

"A mer - ry, mer - ry Christ - mas To all, this Christ - mas Day!"

111 SHINE, LITTLE CANDLES

MAUD LINDSAY

ELSIE A. MERRIMAN

1. Shine, lit - tle can - dles, Shine, stars a - bove,
2. Poor was the sta - ble Where he was born;
3. No pil - low had he, No bed but hay;
4. Shine, lit - tle can - dles, Shine, stars a - bove,

Prais - ing the Christ - child, God's gift of love.
Cows watched his sleep - ing That won - drous morn.
Yet heav - en's glo - ry Shone where he lay.
Prais - ing the Christ - child, God's gift of love.

112   ## WHAT CAN BABY DO

(The activities of the growing child may suggest other stanzas in similar form.)

Lucy E. Low   English Folk-song

What can ba - by do, Oh, what can ba - by do? Just pat - a - cake, and

pat - a - cake, And play at peek - a - boo. And play at peek - a - boo, And

play at peek-a-boo; Just pat - a - cake and pat - a - cake, And play at peek-a-boo.

Used by permission

113   THE PLEASANT DARK

A BEDTIME SONG

SARAH GRAMES CLARK   GRACE WILBUR CONANT

Softly, in a crooning fashion

1. The cun-ning lit-tle bird-ies, with their moth-ers in the
2. fun-ny lit-tle rab-bits, with their moth-ers safe from
3. hap-py lit-tle children, when they're tucked in-to their

nest, Love the dark, the friend-ly dark. The
sight, Love the dark, the friend-ly dark. They
beds, Love the dark, the friend-ly dark. They

heaven-ly Fa-ther sends it and it gives them qui-et rest. He makes the dark,
cud-dle down so hap-pi-ly when God puts out the light, And makes it dark,
know the soft gray cur-tain that God hangs a-bove their heads Is just the dark,

the pleas - ant dark.   2. The
the pleas - ant dark.   3. And
the pleas - ant (*Omit . . . .*) dark.

114   WHAT DOES THE CLOCK SAY?

Words and music by EDNA M. SHAW

What does the clock say? Tick, tick, tick;   All the night and all the day, Tick, tick, tick;

Tick, tick, tick, tick, tick, tick, tick, — Lis - ten and you'll hear it say, Tick, tick, tick.

Used by permission

115 SOFTLY BLOWS THE WIND

G. W. C.

FERD. HILLER

1. Soft - ly blows the wind of the west! . All the lit - tle
2. Soft - ly blows the wind of the west! . All the lit - tle

birds are sleep - ing, And the night comes slow - ly creep - ing; Moth - er's own
lambs are sleep - ing, In their wool - ly moth-ers' keep - ing; Moth - er's own

bird . is safe in its nest, . is safe in its nest. .
lamb . may qui - et - ly rest, . may qui - et - ly rest. .

Words used by permission

THE BROWN MOTHER HEN

R. A. MINTER

Bohemian Folk-song

Con moto

1. Down in the farm - yard, see, there are chick-ens ten, Out for a
2. Down in the farm - yard, see, there are chick-ens ten, Seek-ing their
3. Down in the farm - yard, see, there are chick-ens ten, Tak-ing a

walk with the brown moth - er hen. Ten down-y lit - tle chick -ens! Proud is she
din - ner with wise moth - er hen,— Ten ea - ger lit - tle chick -ens, An - swer-ing
rest with the good moth - er hen. Ten tir - ed lit - tle chick -ens Snug - gle them

then, Step-ping so state-ly, the brown mother hen; Step-ping, and stop-ping, and
when Called to come quick-ly by wise moth-er hen; Scratch-ing, and cluck-ing, and
then Un - der the feath-ers of good moth-er hen; Warm-ly and soft - ly she

step-ping a - gain, "Fol - low me, chicks," says the brown moth-er hen.
scratch-ing a - gain, "Din - ner is served," says the wise moth-er hen.
broods them a - gain Un - der her wings, does the good moth-er hen.

CHILDREN'S ORIGINAL TUNES
ILLUSTRATIVE OF A VALUABLE FORM OF SELF-EXPRESSION

117

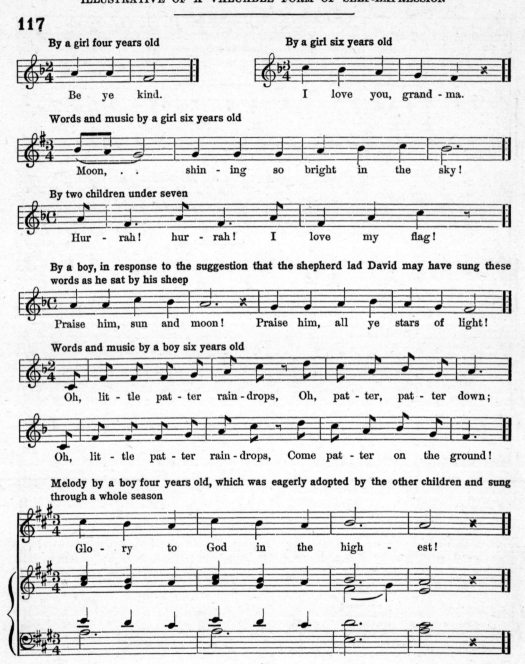

By a girl four years old

Be ye kind.

By a girl six years old

I love you, grand - ma.

Words and music by a girl six years old

Moon, . . shin - ing so bright in the sky!

By two children under seven

Hur - rah! hur - rah! I love my flag!

By a boy, in response to the suggestion that the shepherd lad David may have sung these words as he sat by his sheep

Praise him, sun and moon! Praise him, all ye stars of light!

Words and music by a boy six years old

Oh, lit - tle pat - ter rain - drops, Oh, pat - ter, pat - ter down;

Oh, lit - tle pat - ter rain - drops, Come pat - ter on the ground!

Melody by a boy four years old, which was eagerly adopted by the other children and sung through a whole season

Glo - ry to God in the high - est!

118   CAREFUL WORKMEN

ALFARATA HILTON

A. B. PONSONBY

1. Dear Lord, who shaped our world so fair And set the stars on high, ... Oh, make us care- ful work- men too, In ev- ery- thing we try! ..

2. Oh, help us faith- ful- ly to do The work we start to- day, ... So this may be a joy to see, And wor- thy thee, we pray! ..

119 WE'RE GLAD TO SAY GOOD MORNING

Words and music by GRACE WILBUR CONANT

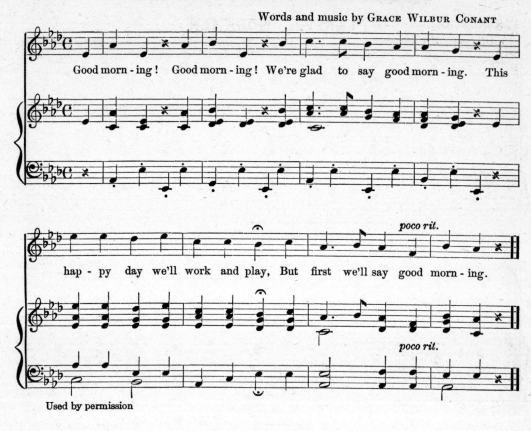

Good morn-ing! Good morn-ing! We're glad to say good morn-ing. This

hap-py day we'll work and play, But first we'll say good morn-ing.

Used by permission

120 JOY SONG

KATHERINE MERRILL

German Air

My heart is so full of joy to-day I'm hap-py in work and song and play.

Used by permission

SING WHILE YOU'RE WORKING

Frances Weld Danielson

French Air

Sing while you're work-ing, Work while you sing, All in time to mu-sic.

Let your voic-es ring! Sing while you're work-ing, Don't for-get the

song; The day you are sing-ing, Work will not seem long.

poco rit.

DID YOU EVER SEE A LASSIE

Did you ev-er see a lass-ie, a lass-ie, a lass-ie, Did you

ev-er see a lass-ie do *this* way and *that?* Do *this* way and *that* way, and

this way and *that* way, Did you ev-er see a lass-ie do *this* way and *that?*

Preparation. Players form circle, joining hands. Child stands in center as leader.

Action. Players walk around in the circle. At the words, "do *this* way and *that*," leader makes some movement. Players imitate this while singing last two lines. Leader chooses a child to take her place. (When a boy leads the word "laddie" is used.)

THE FARMER IN THE DELL

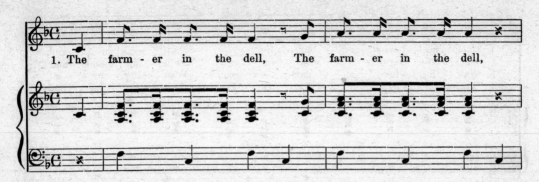

1. The farm-er in the dell, The farm-er in the dell,

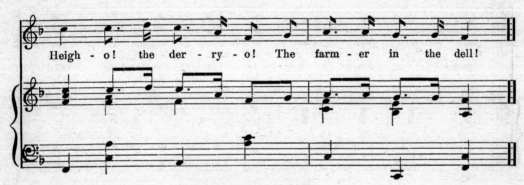

Heigh - o! the der - ry - o! The farm - er in the dell!

2 The farmer takes a wife,
  The farmer takes a wife,
    Heigh-o! the derry-o!
  The farmer takes a wife.

3 The wife takes a child, etc.

4 The child takes a nurse, etc.

5 The nurse takes a dog, etc.

6 The dog takes a cat, etc.

7 The cat takes a rat, etc.

8 The rat takes a cheese, etc.

9 The cheese stands alone, etc.

Preparation. Players form circle, joining hands. Child goes to center as the farmer.

First Stanza. Circle skips or walks to left.

Second-Eighth Stanzas. Farmer chooses a wife from the circle; wife, a child; child, a nurse; and so on. Circle continues moving. Music stops after eighth stanza. All but the cheese leave the center.

Ninth Verse. Players stand and clap.

OATS, PEAS, BEANS AND BARLEY GROW

1. Oats, peas, beans and bar - ley grow, Oats, peas, beans and bar - ley grow, Can you .. or I or an - y one know How oats, peas, beans and bar - ley grow?
2. Thus the farm - er sows his seed, Thus he stands and takes his ease; ... Stamps . his foot and claps . his hands And turns a - round to view his lands.
3. Wait - ing for a part - ner, Wait - ing for a part - ner, ... O - pen the ring and choose one in, While we all gai - ly dance and sing.
4. Tra, la, la, la la, la, la; Tra, la, la, la, la, la, la; Tra, la, .. la, la, la, la, .. la, la; Tra, la, la, la, la, la, la, la!

Preparation. Players form circle, joining hands. Child goes to center as the farmer.

First Stanza. Players walk to left.

Second Stanza. Players stand and act out the words.

Third Stanza. Farmer chooses a partner.

Fourth Stanza. Circle skips to left. Farmer and partner skip to right.

Repetition. Farmer and partner stay in center. Both choose partners in third stanza, and game is repeated.

HERE WE GO ROUND THE MULBERRY BUSH

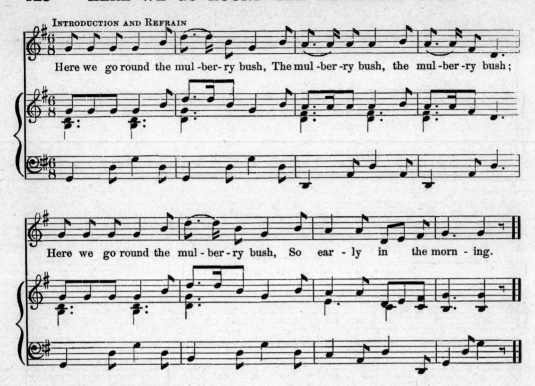

INTRODUCTION AND REFRAIN

Here we go round the mul-ber-ry bush, The mul-ber-ry bush, the mul-ber-ry bush;

Here we go round the mul-ber-ry bush, So ear-ly in the morn-ing.

1 This is the way we wash our clothes,
We wash our clothes, we wash our clothes,
This is the way we wash our clothes,
So early Monday morning. REF.

2 This is the way we iron our clothes,
We iron our clothes, we iron our clothes,
This is the way we iron our clothes,
So early Tuesday morning. REF.

3 This is the way we mend our clothes,
We mend our clothes, we mend our clothes,
This is the way we mend our clothes,
So early Wednesday morning. REF.

4 This is the way we sweep the house,
We sweep the house, we sweep the house,

This is the way we sweep the house,
So early Thursday morning. REF.

5 This is the way we scrub the floor,
We scrub the floor, we scrub the floor,
This is the way we scrub the floor,
So early Friday morning. REF.

6 This is the way we knead our bread,
We knead our bread, we knead our bread,
This is the way we knead our bread,
So early Saturday morning. REF.

7 This is the way we go to church,
We go to church, we go to church,
This is the way we go to church,
So early Sunday morning. REF.

Preparation. Players form circle and join hands.

Introduction and Refrain. Circle skips to left.

Stanzas. Players drop hands and act out the words.

CAROUSEL
MERRY-GO-ROUND

Preparation. Players form double circle, facing center. Inner circle joins hands. Outer circle places hands on shoulders of those in front.

Measures 1-4. Circles move slowly to left.

Measures 5-7. Circles move more quickly.

Measures 8-11, repeated. Circles move rapidly, first to left, then to right.

Repetition. Circles change places and the game is repeated.

127   # TODAY'S THE FIRST OF MAY

1. To - day's the first of May, To - day's the first of May, May, May;
2. Good - bye, good - bye, my friend, We'll meet a - gain some day, some day;

To - day's the first of May, To - day's the first of May.
We'll meet a - gain some day, Be - fore the first of May.

Preparation. Players form double circle, facing left, and take partners' hands.

First Stanza. Players skip forward, swinging arms.

Second Stanza. Line 1. Players face partners and shake hands. Lines 2, 3 and 4. Outer circle skips to left. Inner circle skips to right.

Repetition. Inner circle faces left. Players take hands of children opposite, and game is repeated.

ROUND AND ROUND THE VILLAGE

1. Round and round the vil-lage, Round and round the vil-lage,
2. In and out the win-dows, In and out the win-dows,
3. Stand and face your part-ner, Stand and face your part-ner,
4. Fol-low me to Lon-don, Fol-low me to Lon-don,

Round and round the vil-lage, As fast as we can go.
In and out the win-dows, As we have done be-fore.
Stand and face your part-ner, And bow be-fore you go.
Fol-low me to Lon-don, As we have done be-fore.

Preparation. Children form circle, joining hands and facing center. Several children rema㐇 outside.

First Stanza. Children outside run around circle to left.

Second Stanza. Children in circle raise arms. Runners pass under arches thus formed.

Third Stanza. Runners choose and bow to partners. Children in circle drop arms.

Fourth Stanza. Partners cross hands and skip outside circle. Children in circle skip.

Repetition. Game is repeated, till all in the circle are chosen.

HERE WE GO LOOBY LOO

INTRODUCTION AND REFRAIN

Here we go loo-by loo, Here we go loo-by light, Here we go loo-by loo, All on a Sat-ur-day night. 1. Put your right hand in, Put your right hand out, Give your right hand a shake, shake, shake, And turn your-self a-bout.

Fine

D.C.

2 Put your left hand in, etc.
3 Put your right foot in, etc.
4 Put your left foot in, etc.
5 Put your head 'way in, etc.
6 Put your whole self in, etc.

Preparation. Players form circle, joining hands.
Introduction and Refrain. All skip around in the circle.
Stanzas. Players act out the words.

130   HIDE THE SLIPPER

(A blindfolded child stands in the center of a circle of children sitting close together. As the first stanza is sung a slipper is passed from one to another, underneath them. The child in the center has the bandage removed and bows before the child he guesses has the slipper, during the singing of the second stanza.)

F. W. D.

Slav Folk-song

1. Round the ring, while we sing, Goes the slip - per slid - ing,
2. Make your bow; tell us now Where the slip - per's hid - ing.

Round the ring, while we sing, Goes the slip - per slid - ing.
Make your bow; tell us now Where the slip - per's hid - ing.

131   FOLLOW MY LEADER

F. W. D.

Children's Singing Game from Languedoc

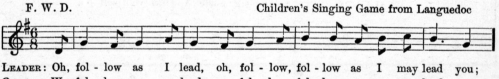

LEADER: Oh, fol - low as I lead, oh, fol - low, fol - low as I may lead you;
OTHERS: We fol - low as you lead, we fol - low, fol - low as you may lead us;

Oh, fol - low as I lead, oh, fol - low me, as I may lead. .
We fol - low as you lead, we fol - low you, as you may lead. .

132   WHO HAS GONE

GUESSING GAME

(A blindfolded child stands in the center of the circle while a child leaves the room. The bandage is removed, and the others sing the question. The child sings the answer. If he has guessed right, all clap and sing the invitation. If he cannot guess, he is blindfolded again.)

F. W. D.   Children's Singing Game from Languedoc

QUESTION: Who has gone and left our cir - cle? Who has gone? Who has gone?
ANSWER: Ma - ry's gone and left our cir - cle. Ma - ry's gone, Ma - ry's gone.
INVITATION: Ma - ry, come, for he has guessed you. Ma - ry, come! Ma - ry, come!

133   BALL IN RING

(Children sit in a circle, in the center of which is a small ring drawn with chalk. A child holds a ball high, then rolls it, and if it stops within the ring, the song is repeated more loudly, while the children sing tra, la, la, and clap.)

F. W. D.   Children's Singing Game from Languedoc

Now   hold   your   ball   read - y   To   roll   in   the   ring.

Be   care - ful;   roll   quiet - ly;   We   watch   as   we   sing!

134 BALL OR BEAN-BAG GAME

(The children select partners, and form two circles, with two feet between the outer and inner. They move slowly round, tossing and catching balls or bean-bags, as they sing the first two lines. The inner circle takes short steps to keep opposite partners. Directions in the third and fourth lines beginning, "Stop, and turn," are followed, and the children move in the opposite direction while they sing the fifth and sixth lines and begin the song again.)

F. W. D.   Children's Singing Game from Montpellier, France

Oh, here we go round and toss our balls/bags } Here we go round a-gain!

Oh, here we go round and toss our balls/bags } Just as we went be-fore!

Stop, and turn, and face your part-ner; Toss to him, and turn once more.

Words copyright, 1925, by SIDNEY A. WESTON. Music used by permission

135 ROUND AND ROUND MY HANDS ARE WHIRLING
GUESSING GAME

(A child within the circle approaches some child on the ring, whirling before him his closed hands in one of which some small object is hidden. He presents his closed fists to the child on the ring, who touches one of his hands. If the latter has guessed correctly, he takes possession of the object, goes within the circle while the first child takes his place on the ring, and the game proceeds as before. If the guess is not correct, the first child continues until some one succeeds. The words need not be sung every time, as the rhythm is sufficient to sustain the game.)

GERTRUDE MAYNARD   French Air

Round and round my hands are whirl-ing, Round and round my hands are

Used by permission

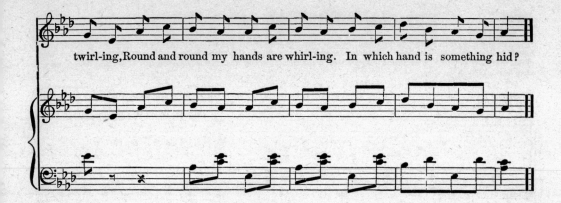

twirl-ing, Round and round my hands are whirl-ing. In which hand is something hid?

136   BOUNCE THE BALL

(The children bounce balls, and sing while moving in a circle. They then run lightly on the tips of their toes, first to the left, then to the right, still in circle formation.)

F. W. D.   Cossack Folk-tune

Bounce the ball, oh, bounce the ball and catch it, Bounce the ball, oh, bounce the ball!

137   MUSICAL CHAIRS OR MUSICAL RUG

(Chairs are placed in a row, alternate ones facing the same way, and one less in number than the players. A march is begun around the chairs. Every now and then the music suddenly stops, and the children sit down. The child who fails to find a seat drops out, a chair is taken away, and the march is resumed. The child who gets a seat in the last chair wins.

(Players march around in a circle to music, crossing a rug, large enough so that a child cannot jump over it. When the music stops without warning those children found with one or both feet on the rug drop out of the game. This continues till only one child is marching, who is therefore the winner.)

Old French Wedding Music

138   THE WEATHER-VANE

(The teacher, or a child, impersonates the weather-vane and sings the second stanza.)

A. B. P.   Slav Folk-song

CHILDREN: Tell us what you're do-ing up there,— We would be learn-ing
WEATHER-VANE: With the wind I'm bus-y up here. Would you be know-ing

Why . you're turn-ing, Weath-er-vane, so bus-y up there!
Which way 'tis blow-ing, I can al-ways show you up here.

Used by permission

139   **I HAVE A LITTLE PONY**

(The children drive each other about while the teacher and other children sing the song. They may act out the feeding, and tying on the " fluffy bow," and the driving may be fast or slow, according to the music.)

BERTHA M. RHODES   Old German Air

1. I have a lit-tle po-ny; I'll feed him well with gold-en grain;
2. I'll buy a silk-en rib-bon And tie in-to a fluf-fy bow

I'll drive him to the coun-try And drive him home a-gain.
To deck my lit-tle po-ny, Be-cause I love him so.

Used by permission

140   **SAFETY SONG**

(Children act this in pantomime.)

CARL McKAY, Grade 4-A   AGNES K. BAKER
Fremont School, Alhambra, California

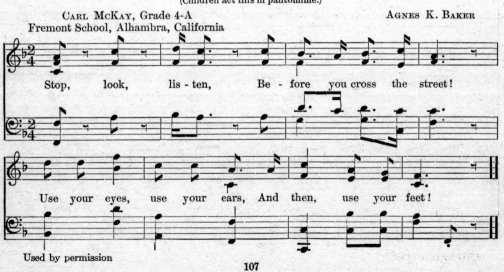

Stop, look, lis-ten, Be-fore you cross the street!

Use your eyes, use your ears, And then, use your feet!

Used by permission

BLACK HORSE, BROWN HORSE

(Trotting and galloping)

Nancy Byrd Turner

Grace Wilbur Conant

Black horse, brown horse, roan horse, gray,

Trit - trot, trit - trot, off and a - way! Gray horse, roan horse,

brown horse, black, Pit - a - pat, pit - a - pat, now we can - ter back!

Used by permission

THE BUTTERFLY

SONG WITH IMPERSONATION

Herbert Scholfield

Melody by D. S. and J. F.

But-ter-fly, But-ter-fly, Pret-ty gold-en but-ter-fly, But-ter-fly a-float-ing O'er the gar-den high, Play with me, Stay with me, Love-ly but-ter-fly!

Leggiero

The butterfly flits about

leggierissimo

Used by permission

THE COBBLER

Bertha M. Rhodes

French Folk-song

Acc. leggiero

Rhythm for hammering

1. Oh, the kind old cob - bler works a - way With his piec - es stout of leath - er;
2. When the kind old cob - bler mends a shoe Oh, he sews the rips to - geth - er

And his ham - mer sings a "rap - a - tap - a - tap," For he's bus - y all the day.
With a dou - ble thread, and "rap - a - tap - a - tap," It is just as good as new.

Used by permission

144
LIGHTHOUSE ON THE ROCKS
(This song may be dramatized.)

GRACE WILBUR CONANT

Bohemian Folk-song

CHILD: Light-house on the rocks by the roll-ing green sea,
LIGHTHOUSE: I must help the sail-ors all through the dark night.

Tell me why you stand there, firm and stead-y, Hold-ing high your lan-tern,
That is why I stand here, firm and stead-y, Hold-ing high my lan-tern,

al-ways read-y,—Light-house on the rocks by the roll-ing green sea.
al-ways read-y; I must help the sail-ors, all through the dark night.

Used by permission

145   THE CHILDREN'S MARCH

Grace Wilbur Conant

With strong and steady rhythm

D.C. al Fine

146   ## ON CHRISTMAS DAY IN THE MORNING

MARCH

Old English Song, "I saw three ships"

Arrangement from *Father Finn's Carol Book*, C. C. BIRCHARD & Co., Publishers, Boston

147

OLD SCANDINAVIAN SONG

(May be used as a march)

148

SLAV FOLK-SONG

(May be used as a march, or for rhythmic exercises)

STRAIGHT AND STEADY

MARCH

Grace Wilbur Conant

ALERTNESS ("I'm all ready!")

SCHUMANN, Op. 68

JOYOUSNESS ("What fun we are having!")

Norwegian Folk-song

ENERGY ("I want to work.")

Old Song

SELF-CONFIDENCE ("I can do it.")

G. W. C.

Con moto

FRIENDLINESS ("I like people.")

German Folk-song

Allegro moderato

CURIOSITY ("*What* is it?")

G. W. C.

Allegretto

poco rit.

117

HAPPINESS ("'The world is such a happy place!'")

Vivace G. W. C.

CONFIDENCE ("I'm not afraid any more.")

Andante Haydn

REVERENCE ("'Surely the Lord is in this place.'")

Larghetto From a German Chorale

INDEX OF FIRST LINES